A Child's Primer
of Natural History

A Child's Primer of Natural History

By Oliver Herford

with Pictures by
the Author

Dover Publications, Inc., New York

Published in Canada by General Publishing Company, Ltd., 30 Lesmill Road, Don Mills, Toronto, Ontario.

Published in the United Kingdom by Constable and Company, Ltd., 10 Orange Street, London W.C. 2.

This Dover edition, first published in 1966, is an unabridged and unaltered republication of the work originally published by Charles Scribner's Sons in 1899.

Library of Congress Catalog Card Number: 66-23391

Manufactured in the United States of America
Dover Publications, Inc.
180 Varick Street
New York, N.Y. 10014

Contents

	PAGE		PAGE
A Seal	3	The Ant	39
The Giraffe	7	An Arctic Hare	43
The Yak	11	The Wolf	47
A Whale	15	An Ostrich	51
The Leopard	19	The Hippopotamus	55
The Sloth	23	The Fly	59
The Elephant	27	The Mongoos	63
The Pig-Pen	31	The Platypus	67
Some Geese	35	The Chimpanzee	71

Contents—*Continued*

	PAGE			PAGE
A Mole	75	The Cat	87
The Rhinoceros .	79	The Dog . . .	91
A Penguin . . .	83	A Chameleon . .	95

A Seal.

A Seal.

SEE, chil-dren, the Fur-bear-ing Seal;
Ob-serve his mis-di-rect-ed zeal:
He dines with most ab-ste-mi-ous care
On Fish, Ice Water and Fresh Air
A-void-ing cond-i-ments or spice,
For fear his fur should not be nice
And fine and smooth and soft and meet
For Broad-way or for Re-gent Street
And yet some-how I of-ten feel
(Though for the kind Fur-bear-ing Seal
I har-bor a Re-spect Pro-found)
He runs Fur-bear-ance in the ground.

The Giraffe.

The Giraffe.

SEE the Gi-raffe; he is so tall
There is not room to get him all
U-pon the page. His head is high-er—
The pic-ture proves it—than the Spire.
That 's why the na-tives, when they race
To catch him, call it stee-ple-chase.
His chief de-light it is to set
A good example: shine or wet
He rises ere the break of day,
And starts his break-fast right away.
His food has such a way to go,—
His throat 's so very long,—and so

                              An early

An early break-fast he must munch
To get it down ere time for lunch.

The Yak.

The Yak.

THIS is the Yak, so neg-li-gée:
His coif-fure 's like a stack of hay;
He lives so far from Any-where,
I fear the Yak neg-lects his hair,
And thinks, since there is none to see,
What mat-ter how un-kempt he be.
How would he feel if he but knew
That in this Pic-ture-book I drew
His Phys-i-og-no-my un-shorn,
For chil-dren to de-ride and scorn?

A Whale.

A Whale.

THE con-sci-en-tious art-ist tries
On-ly to draw what meets his eyes.
This is the Whale; he seems to be
A spout of wa-ter in the sea.
Now, Hux-ley from one bone could make
An un-known beast; so if I take
This spout of wa-ter, and from thence
Con-struct a Whale by in-fer-ence,
A Whale, I ven-ture to as-sert,
Must be an an-i-mat-ed squirt!
Thus, chil-dren, we the truth may sift
By use of Log-ic's Price-less Gift.

The Leopard.

The Leopard.

THIS is the Le-o-pard, my child;
His tem-per 's any-thing but mild.
The Le-o-pard can 't change his spots,
And that—so say the Hot-ten-tots—
Is why he is so wild.
Year in, year out, he may not change,
No mat-ter how the wea-ther range,
From cold to hot. No won-der, child,
We hear the Le-o-pard is wild.

The Sloth.

The Sloth.

THE Sloth en-joys a life of Ease;
He hangs in-vert-ed from the trees,
　　And views life up-side down.
If you, my child, are noth-ing loath
To live in In-dol-ence and Sloth,
　　Un-heed-ing the World's frown,
You, too, un-vexed by Toil and Strife,
May take a hu-mor-ous view of life.

The Elephant.

The Elephant.

THIS is the El-e-phant, who lives
With but one aim—to please.
His i-vo-ry tusk he free-ly gives
To make pi-a-no keys.
One grief he has—how-e'er he tries,
He nev-er can for-get
That one of his e-nor-mous size
Can't be a house-hold pet.
Then does he to his grief give way,
Or sink 'neath sor-row's ban?
Oh, no; in-stead he spends each day
Con-tri-ving some un-sel-fish way
To be of use to Man.

PIANOS

27

The Pig-Pen.

The Pig-Pen.

Oh, turn not from the hum-ble Pig,
My child, or think him in-fra dig.
We oft hear lit-er-a-ry men
Boast of the in-flu-ence of the Pen ;
Yet when we read in His-to-ry's Page
Of Hu-man Pigs in ev-er-y age,
From Crœ-sus to the pres-ent day,
Is it, my child, so hard to say
(De-spite the Scribes' vain-glo-ri-ous boast)
What Pen has in-flu-enced Man the most?

31

Some Geese.

Some Geese.

Ev-er-y child who has the use
Of his sen-ses knows a goose.
See them un-der-neath the tree
Gath-er round the goose-girl's knee,
While she reads them by the hour
From the works of Scho-pen-hau-er.
How pa-tient-ly the geese at-tend!
But do they re-al-ly com-pre-hend
What Scho-pen-hau-er 's driv-ing at?
Oh, not at all; but what of that?
Nei-ther do I; nei-ther does she;
And, for that mat-ter, nor does he.

The Ant.

The Ant.

My child, ob-serve the use-ful **Ant,**
How hard she works each day.
She works as hard as ad-a-mant
(That 's very hard, they say).
She has no time to gal-li-vant;
She has no time to play.
Let Fido chase his tail all day;
Let Kitty play at tag:
She has no time to throw a-way,
She has no tail to wag.
She scurries round from morn till night;
She ne-ver, ne-ver sleeps;

She seiz-es

She seiz-es ev-ery-thing in sight,
And drags it home with all her might,
And all she takes she keeps.

An Arctic Hare.

An Arctic Hare.

AN Arc-tic Hare we now be-hold.
  The hair, you will ob-serve, is white;
But if you think the Hare is old,
  You will be ver-y far from right.
The Hare is young, and yet the hair
  Grew white in but a sin-gle night.
Why, then it must have been a scare
  That turned this Hare. No; 't was not fright
(Al-though such cases are well known);
  I fear that once a-gain you 're wrong.
Know then, that in the Arc-tic Zone
  A sin-gle night is six months long.

The Wolf.

The Wolf.

Oh, yes, the Wolf is bad, it 's true;
But how with-out him could we do?
If there were not a wolf, what good
Would be the tale of Rid-ing-hood?
The Lit-tle Child from sin will fly
When told the wick-ed Wolf is nigh;
And when, ar-rived at Man's es-tate,
He hears the Wolf out-side his gate,
He knows it 's time to put a-way
I-dle fri-vol-i-ty and play.
That 's how (but do not men-tion it)
This prim-er hap-pened to be writ.

An Ostrich.

An Ostrich.

THIS is an Os-trich. See him stand:
His head is bur-ied in the sand.
It is not that he seeks for food,
Nor is he shy, nor is he rude;
But he is sen-si-tive, and shrinks
And hides his head when-e'er he thinks
How, on the Gains-bor-ough hat some day
Of some fine la-dy at the play,
His fea-thers may ob-struct the view
Of all the stage from me or you.

The Hippopotamus.

The Hippopotamus.

"Oh, say, what is this fearful, wild
In-cor-ri-gible cuss?"
"This *crea-ture* (don't say 'cuss,' my child;
'T is slang)—this crea-ture fierce is styled
The Hip-po-pot-am-us.
His curious name de-rives its source
From two Greek words: *hippos*—a horse,
Potamos—river. See?
The river 's plain e-nough, of course;
But why they called *that* thing a *horse*,
That 's what is Greek to me."

The Fly.

The Fly.

OB-SERVE, my child, the House-hold Fly,
With his ex-traor-di-na-ry eye:
What-ev-er thing he may be-hold
Is mul-ti-plied a thou-sand-fold.
We do not need a com-plex eye
When we ob-serve the House-hold Fly:
He is so vol-a-tile that he
In *ev-er-y* place at once can be;
He is the buzz-ing in-car-na-tion
Of an-i-mate mul-ti-pli-ca-tion.
Ah! chil-dren, who can tell the Why
And Where-fore of the House-hold Fly?

59

The Mongoos.

The Mongoos.

THIS, Chil-dren, is the famed Mon-goos.
He has an ap-pe-tite ab-struse;
Strange to re-late, this crea-ture takes
A cu-ri-ous joy in eat-ing snakes—
All kinds, though, it must be con-fessed,
He likes the poi-son-ous ones the best.
From him we learn how ve-ry small
A thing can bring a-bout a Fall.
Oh, Mon-goos, where were you that day
When Mis-tress Eve was led a-stray?
If you 'd but seen the ser-pent first,
Our Parents would not have been cursed,
                              And so

The Platypus.

The Platypus.

My child, the Duck-billed Plat-y-pus
A sad ex-am-ple sets for us :
From him we learn how In-de-ci-sion
Of char-ac-ter pro-vokes De-ri-sion.
This vac-il-lat-ing Thing, you see,
Could not de-cide which he would be,
Fish, Flesh, or Fowl, and chose all three.
The sci-en-tists were sore-ly vexed
To clas-si-fy him; so per-plexed
Their brains that they, with Rage at bay,
Called him a hor-rid name one day,—
A name that baf-fles, frights, and shocks us,—
Or-ni-tho-rhyn-chus Par-a-dox-us.

The Chimpanzee.

The Chimpanzee.

Chil-dren, be-hold the Chim-pan-zee:
He sits on the an-ces-tral tree
From which we sprang in ag-es gone.
I 'm glad we sprang: had we held on,
We might, for aught that I can say,
Be hor-rid Chim-pan-zees to-day.

A Mole.

A Mole.

Sᴇᴇ, chil-dren, the mis-guid-ed Mole.
He lives down in a deep, dark hole;
Sweet-ness, and Light, and good Fresh Air
Are things for which he does not care.
He has not e-ven that make-shift
Of fee-ble minds—the *so-cial gift*.
But say not that he has no soul,
Lest hap-ly we mis-judge the Mole;
Nay, if we mea-sure him by Men,
No doubt he sits in his dark den
In-struct-ing oth-ers blind as he
Ex-act-ly how the world *should* be.

The Rhinoceros.

The Rhinoceros.

So this is the Rhi-no-ce-ros!
I won-der why he looks so cross.
Per-haps he is an-noyed a bit
Be-cause his cloth-ing does not fit.
(They say he got it read-y made!)
It is not that, I am a-fraid.
He looks so cross be-cause I drew
Him with one horn in-stead of two.

Well, since he cares so much for style,
Let 's give him two and see him smile.

A Penguin.

A Penguin.

The Pen-guin sits up-on the shore
And loves the lit-tle fish to bore;
He has one en-er-vat-ing joke
That would a very Saint pro-voke:
"The *Pen*-guin 's might-i-er than the *Sword*-fish";
He tells this dai-ly to the bored fish,
Un-til they are so weak, they float
With-out re-sis-tance down his throat.

The Cat.

The Cat.

OB-SERVE the Cat up-on this page.
Phil-os-o-phers in ev-er-y age,
The ver-y *wis-est* of the wise,
Have tried her mind to an-a-lyze
In vain, for noth-ing can they learn.
She baf-fles them at ev-er-y turn
Like Mis-ter Ham-let in the play.
She leads their rea-son-ing a-stray;
She feigns **an in-ter-est in** string
Or yarn or any roll-ing thing.
Un-like the **Dog,** she does not care
With com-mon Man her thoughts to share.

She teach-es

She teach-es us that in life's walk
'T is bet-ter to let oth-ers talk,
And lis-ten while *they* say in-stead
The fool-ish things *we* might have **said.**

The Dog.

The Dog.

HERE is the Dog. Since time be-gan,
The Dog has been the friend of MAN,
The Dog loves MAN be-cause he shears
His coat and clips his tail and ears.
MAN loves the Dog be-cause he 'll stay
And lis-ten to his talk all day,
And wag his tail and show de-light
At all his jokes, how-ev-er trite.
His bark is far worse than his bite,
So peo-ple say. They may be right;
Yet if to make a choice I had,
I 'd choose his bark, how-ev-er bad.

A Chameleon.

A Chameleon.

A USE-FUL les-son you may con,
My Child, from the Cha-me-le-on :
He has the gift, ex-treme-ly rare
In an-i-mals, of sav-oir-faire.
And if the se-cret you would guess
Of the Cha-me-le-on's suc-cess,
A-dapt your-self with great-est care
To your sur-round-ings ev-er-y-where ;
And then, un-less your sex pre-vent,
Some day you may be Pres-i-dent.